How do I use this scheme?

Key Words with Peter and Jane has three
parallel series, each containing twelve books. All three
series are written using the same carefully controlled
vocabulary. Readers will get the most out of **Key Words** with
Peter and Jane when they follow the books in the pattern
1a, 1b, 1c; 2a, 2b, 2c and so on.

• Series a
gradually introduces and repeats new words.

• Series b
provides further practice of these same words, but
in a different context and with different illustrations.

• Series c
uses familiar words to teach **phonics** in a methodical way,
enabling children to read increasingly difficult words.
It also provides a link to writing.

LADYBIRD BOOKS

UK | USA | Canada | Ireland | Australia
India | New Zealand | South Africa

Ladybird Books is part of the Penguin Random House group of companies
whose addresses can be found at global.penguinrandomhouse.com.

www.penguin.co.uk   www.puffin.co.uk   www.ladybird.co.uk

First published 1964
This edition 2009, 2014, 2016
Copyright © Ladybird Books Ltd, 1964
001

A CIP catalogue record for this book is
available from the British Library

ISBN: 978-1-409-30121-9

Printed in China

Key Words

with Peter and Jane

4c

Say the sound

written by W. Murray
illustrated by J.H. Wingfield

We can read the words—

boy

ball

boat

bus

Look at each picture and make the sound of the letter.

b

b

b

b

We can read the words—

car

cow

cat

cake

Look at each picture and make the sound of the letter.

C

C

C

C

Complete the words as you write them in your exercise book.
The pictures will help you.

b   c

1 – ow

2 – ar

3 – oat

4 – oy

5 – ake

6 – all

7 – us

8 – at

The answers are on Page 50

1

2

3

4

5

6

7

8

We can read the words—

tea

two

top

toys

Look at each picture and make the sound of the letter.

t

t 2

t

t

a

1. An apple.

2. The girl has an apple.

3. The girl draws an apple.
   She writes **a** for apple.
   She makes the sound for **a**.

4. The boy draws an apple.
   He draws **a** for apple.
   He makes the sound for **a**.

Complete the words as you write them
in your exercise book.
The pictures will help you.

b   c   t   a

1 –pple

2 –wo

3 –an

4 –ea

5 –pples

6 –op

7 –oys

8 –ed

The answers are on Page 50

1

2

3

4

5

6

7

8

The girl is at school.

She likes school.

She has some pictures.

She puts the pictures with
the sounds.

"I like to do this," the girl says.
"It helps me to read."

"This helps me to read," says the boy.

He is at school.

He likes school.

The boy has some pictures.

He puts the pictures with the sounds.

Here is a girl at work.

She makes a picture with
the cards.

She makes the sounds for **c**, **a**, **t**.

"**C**, **a**, **t** makes cat," she says.

She draws a cat, and then
she writes.

Here is a boy at work.

He makes a picture with
the cards.

He makes the sounds for **b**, **a**, **t**.

"**B**, **a**, **t** makes bat," he says.

He draws a bat, and then
he writes.

The boy and the girl play a game with the cards.

They play a game with pictures and sounds.

The girl can see the pictures.

The boy can see the letters.

"Point to bat," says the girl.

"Is this it?" says the boy.

"Have a look," she says.

The boy looks at his card.

"Yes," he says, "it has a picture of a bat."

He keeps the card.

"Point to a cat," says the girl.

He points to a card with **c**.

"This is it," he says.

"Yes," says the girl, "that is the one."

We can read the words—

four

five

fire

fish

Look at each picture and make the sound of the letter.

f **4**

f **5**

f

f

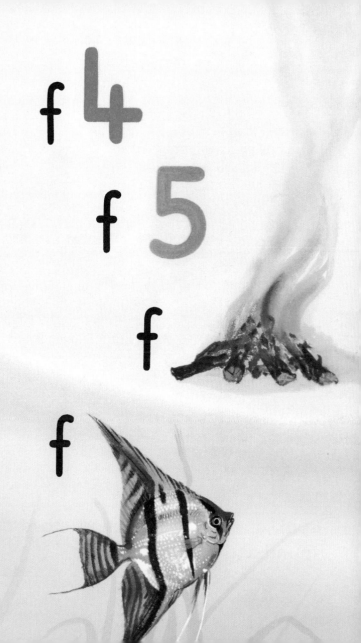

We can read the words—

hat

hand

horse

house

Look at each picture and make the sound of the letter.

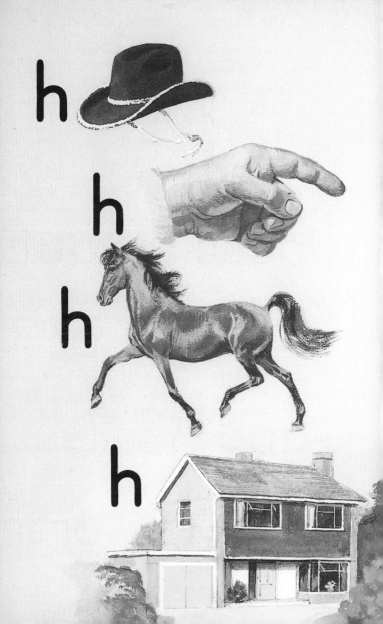

Complete the words as you write them
in your exercise book.
The pictures will help you.

1 – ouse

2 – our

3 – ive

4 – at

5 – and

6 – ish

7 – ire

8 – orse

The answers are on Page 50

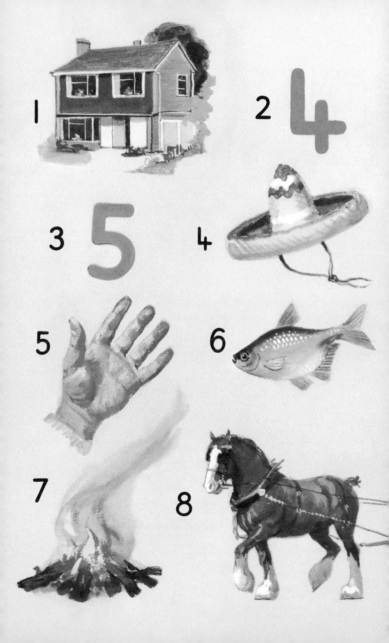

We can read the words—

man

milk

money

men

Look at each picture and make the sound of the letter.

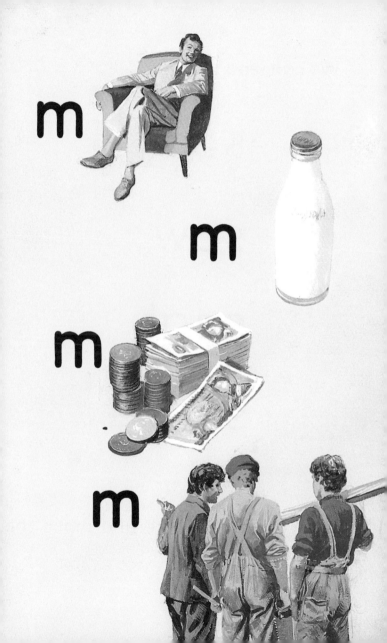

We can read the words—

sea

saw

seat

sun

Look at each picture and make the sound of the letter.

Complete the words as you write them in your exercise book.
The pictures will help you.

m s

1 – un

2 – an

3 – ea

4 – aw

5 – ilk

6 – eat

7 – en

8 – oney

The answers are on Page 50

The girl has some letters.

She makes the sounds of the letters and reads the words.

She reads the word **at**.

Then she makes the sound of the letter **b** and makes **b—at**.

"**B—at** makes bat," she says, "and I see that **c—at** makes cat, **b—all** makes ball, **c—an** makes can, and **b—us** makes bus."

The boy has some letters.

He makes the sounds of the letters and reads the words.

He reads the word **at**.

Then he makes the sound of the letter **h** and makes **h—at**.

"**H—at** makes hat," he says, "and I see that **f—at** makes fat, **h—is** makes his, **r—an** makes ran, and **m—an** makes man."

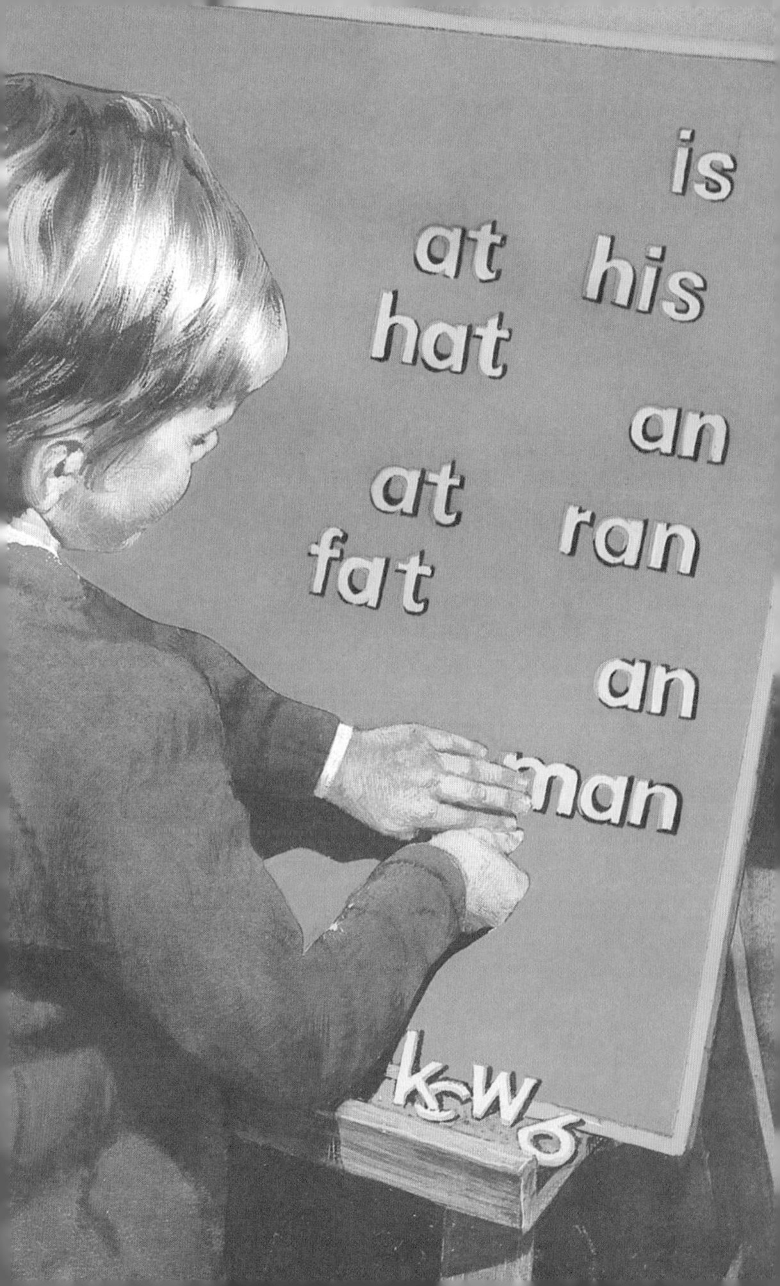

is
at his
hat
an
at ran
fat
an
man
k w

The children all help to make a big fire at the farm. The man lets the boys and girls have some things for the fire.

"We do not want to get into danger," says Jane to the little girl. "We'll keep away."

"There will be no danger," says Peter.

Copy out and complete—

1. The children are — t the farm.

2. They — ake a big fire.

3. The man — elps the children.

4. He gives the children
   — ome things
   for the fire.

The answers are on Page 51

Here is the fire. "It's for us," says Peter. All the children like the big fire.

Jane keeps the little girl with her. They are not in danger.

The dog Pat is here. He is with Jane. He will not jump up or go away.

Copy out and complete—

1. Peter — nd Jane are here.

2. They — an see the fire.

3. They like the — ig fire.

4. They have — un.

The answers are on Page 51

A car stops. The children see it.

"I can see my Dad," says Jane. "He has come to take us home."

They thank Pam and then they all go off home with Dad in his car.

"What fun it was," says Jane to him.

Copy out and complete—

1. They can see the — ar.

2. "Here — omes Dad," says Jane.

3. Dad — akes the children home.

4. "It was — un," says Jane.

The answers are on Page 51

Here are the answers to the written exercises in this book.

Page 8	1	cow	2	car
	3	boat	4	boy
	5	cake	6	ball
	7	bus	8	cat

Page 14	1	apple	2	two
	3	can	4	tea
	5	apples	6	top
	7	toys	8	bed

Page 32	1	house	2	four
	3	five	4	hat
	5	hand	6	fish
	7	fire	8	horse

Page 38	1	sun	2	man
	3	sea	4	saw
	5	milk	6	seat
	7	men	8	money

Page 44 1 The children are at the farm.

2 They make a big fire.

3 The man helps the children.

4 He gives the children some things for the fire.

Page 46 1 Peter and Jane are here.

2 They can see the fire.

3 They like the big fire.

4 They have fun.

Page 49 1 They can see the car.

2 "Here comes Dad," says Jane.

3 Dad takes the children home.

4 "It was fun," says Jane.

Now read Book 5a

Learning by sounds

If children learn the sounds of letters and how to blend them with the other letter sounds (eg. c-a-t) they can tackle new words independently (eg. P-a-t).

In the initial stages it is best if these phonic words are already known to the learner.

However, not all English words can be learned in this way as the English language is not purely phonetic (eg. t-h-e).

In general a 'mixed' approach to reading is recommended. Some words are learned by blending the sounds of their letters and others by look-and-say, whole word or sentence methods.

This book provides the link with writing for the words in Readers 4a and 4b.